SHIPS

around the world

SHIPS
around the world

Written and Illustrated by W.R.R. Hardy

PLATT & MUNK: *Publishers*

Acknowledgements

The author and publisher wish to express their appreciation to the following for their generous help, especially for the numerous photographs which add so much to the book's interest and usefulness.

American President Lines Ltd., Anderson, Green & Co. Ltd., Associated Press, Beken & Son, Brazilian Embassy, British Museum, The British Travel and Holiday Association, Canadian Pacific Railway, Cantieri Riuniti Dell Adriatico, Centrael Fotopersbureau, Consorzio Autonomo Del Porto di Genova, David Baker, David Cheverton & Partners Ltd., Esso Petroleum Company Ltd., Fox Photos Ltd., Ian G. Gilchrist, Harland & Wolff, Group Capt. F. F. Haylock, International News Photos, Japan Information Centre, John Brown & Co. (Clydebank) Ltd., Lockheed Missiles & Space Division, National Maritime Museum, Greenwich, Port of London Authority, The Science Museum, Shell Photographic Unit, Skyfotos, S.C.R. Photo Library, Sport & General, W. H. T. Tayleur, The Times, Union Castle Line, United States Information Service, United States Navy.

Published in 1967 by
The Platt & Munk Company, Inc.
New York, New York 10010

Copyright 1966 by Ward Lock & Co. Ltd. (2778)

Library of Congress Catalog Card Number: 67–10161

Printed in Spain by EDITORIAL FHER, S A.
Bound in the United States of America.

CONTENTS

ships of long ago

When the first primitive man sat astride a fallen tree or simple log and paddled himself forward with his hands, he set in motion a process as important to man's future as the discovery and use of fire and the wheel. This simple act marked the start of shipbuilding and, perhaps of greater significance, the beginning of man's exploration and mastery of the sea and of the unknown land areas of the world.

Although we have no written records or pictures of primitive man's first real boats, we are pretty certain that they were logs rudely carved with stone axes or adzes into simple boat shapes. In fact, they were probably very much like the "dug-outs" still used by native people in the primitive regions of Africa, India, Polynesia and South America. Besides wood, our earliest ancestors used such materials as the reeds and rushes which grew so abundantly on the banks of rivers and lakes. Again, similar craft are still made by native peoples in Africa and South

6

A canoe made of reeds. Boats similar to this are still used on Lake Titicaca on the border of Peru and Bolivia.

America. One of the best known of this type of boat is the "balsa," that is made by the Indians of Peru who live near Lake Titicaca. This, incidentally, is the highest lake in the world, 12,500 feet above sea level.

Egyptians were one of the first peoples to advance the making and sailing of boats to a high degree of skill and performance. This is not surprising, since the life of ancient Egypt depended absolutely on the Nile, not just as a source of irrigation for its crops but as a means of transportation. Unlike primitive man, the Egyptians left pictures of their boats on clay pots and wall paintings. The first of these were painted about 4000 B.C. The earliest Egyptian boats were made of small jointed sections of wood—mainly sycamore and acacia—because no large trees grew in this land of blistering sun and limitless desert. It was not long, however, before the Egyptians began to import timber suitable for building really large boats. In construction these boats were

A drawing of an Egyptian ship on a vase of about 4000 B.C. This is one of the first records of man's conquest of the seas.

7

A dug-out, hollowed out of a tree trunk. This type of craft is still widely used in Africa, India, Polynesia and South America.

"carvels"; that is, the hulls were built of planks laid edge to edge for a smooth outer surface. As early as 3400 B.C. during the reign of Pharaoh Menes the Egyptians were building ships fitted with a sail set amidships and propelled by some twenty to thirty oarsmen and four to six rudder oars. The first seagoing boats were sailed in the Mediterranean—but always in sight of the coast. Generally Egyptian ships were used for carrying merchandise. Some, barges really, were built to carry the large blocks of stone used in the royal palaces and temples. That these barges were used to carry carved stone obelisks which were often well over one hundred feet high gives some idea of their great size. The most magnificent ships built by the Egyptians were undoubtedly the royal galleys which sailed the Mediterranean around 1500 B.C., during the great period in Egypt's long history, the reign of Queen Hatshepsut.

With the decline of Egypt's power the Phoenicians became the ancient world's leading maritime power. They came from the region of Tyre and Sidon, the present coast of Lebanon, and traded their merchandise all over the Mediterranean and even the Atlantic. The best-known Phoenician boat or galley was the "bireme," a vessel with a sail amidships and two banks of oars on each side. The Phoenician merchant ship was not unlike the earlier Egyptian type. What makes the Phoenicians important in marine history is not just their skill as shipbuilders but their skill and daring as sailors and navigators. As early as 465 B.C., Hannon, the Governor of Carthage, led a fleet of some sixty ships, manned by 30,000 men, through the Mediterranean, past the Straits of Gibraltar, and down the west coast of Africa as far as the Gulf of Guinea. Phoenician merchant sailors also ventured into the Atlantic, traveling as far north as Britain to trade glass, metal articles and fabrics for furs and tin.

With the rise and expansion of Greek civilization the Phoenicians' maritime power was destroyed. Although no Greek ship has so far

A photograph of an early coin depicting a Phoenician ship. It is from such finds as this that we are able to reconstruct the vessels which have long since rotted away.

Sea-going boats of the Egyptians, about 3000 B.C.

A Phoenician trading ship, about 1500 B.C.

Longughips of the Vikings on a raid. These
adventuresome-looking ships were some 70 feet long
with a beam of about 17 feet. The sail mast was
just forward of true amidships and there was
provision for 15 pairs of oars. They often had
magnificently carved animal heads at the prow.

been excavated, we know exactly what they looked like
from very accurate stone carvings and paintings on vases.
One of the main types of Greek craft was also called the
bireme—possibly developed from the Phoenicians, but
more powerful and certainly more elaborate. The prow
was fitted with a massive and destructive ram, often
shaped into a giant bird's head. In addition to biremes
the Greeks built "triremes," fighting galleys with three
banks of oars, "quadriremes" with four banks of oars
and "quinqueremes" with five banks of oars.

It was the triremes that defeated the mighty fleet of
Xerxes, the Emperor of Persia. Themistocles, the founder
of the Greek navy, used his 400 triremes to rout completely the 1,000 ships of Xerxes at Salamis, perhaps the
first in a long line of naval battles where skill and cunning
defeated enemies armed with more and greater weapons.

For geographical reasons the Romans were not a
natural naval power, but as their empire grew, naval
and merchant ships became essential. In design the
Roman vessels were similar to those of the Greeks and
Carthaginians, but they were bigger and more elaborate;
some were even being powered by as many as seven
banks of oars. One essentially Roman invention was the
"corvus," a gang-plank equipped with a large metal
spike which fastened onto enemy ships, making it
possible for Roman soldiers to board them easily and
quickly. With the decline of the Empire, the Roman
navy ceased to be important. All its energy and wealth
seem to have been devoted to the construction of pleasure
boats which were examples of magnificent and extrava-

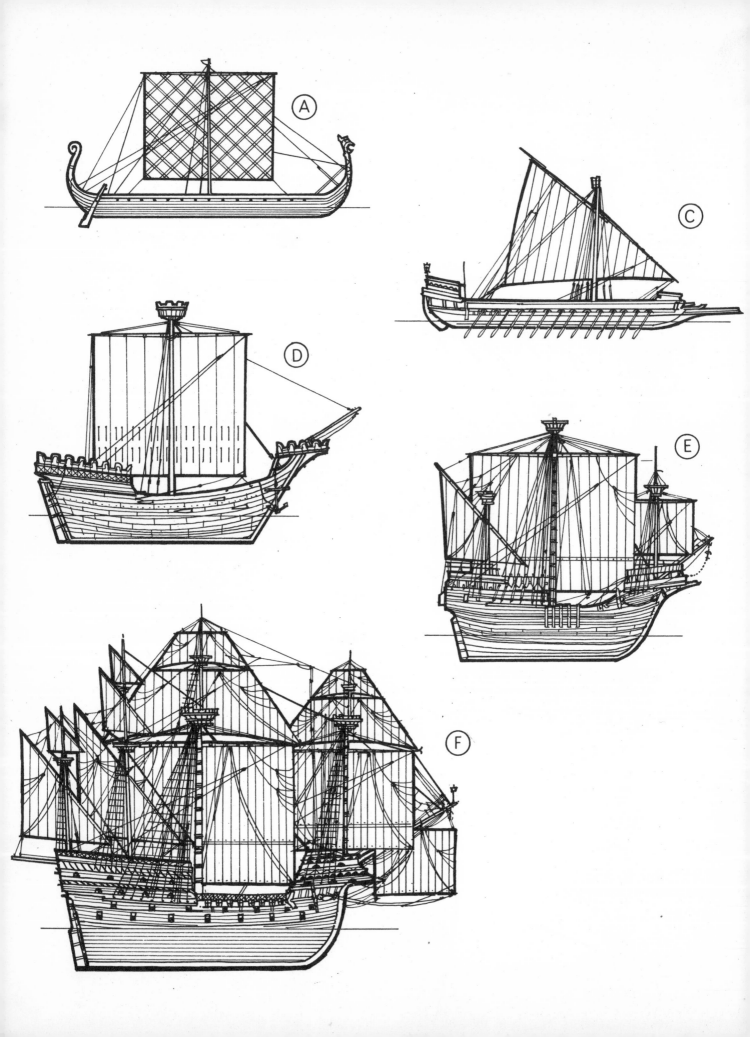

gant opulence. Some of these were, in fact, more like floating palaces than ships. This slothfulness had its due deserts—the destruction of the Roman Empire.

In the cold grey regions of Europe, especially Scandinavia, the land of the Vikings, lived people who were just as skilled at shipbuilding and navigation as the peoples of the sundrenched Mediterranean. Rock-drawings made some 4,000 years ago—and still to be seen in Scandinavia —show that the earliest Scandinavian boats were similar to the "umiak" used today by Eskimos and consisting simply of a light frame covered with animal skin. In Scandinavia this covering was later replaced by wood.

Several original Viking ships have been preserved. One was found near Sandefjord and another at Tonsberg, both in Norway. Both are still very much in their original form. The boat found at Tonsberg, and known as the "Oseberg" ship after the name of the farm on which it was found, is built of oak planks and is 70 feet long, with a beam of about 17 feet. The sail mast is just forward of true amidship and there was provision for 15 pairs of oars.

Although the Vikings are often thought of as raiders, they, too, were just as much traders as the Phoenicians, and built cargo boats, called "knorrs." The Vikings were outstanding navigators who did not just hug coastlines but thrust out into the uncharted seas in search of new

13

A Roman relief carving of a small merchant vessel controlled with a steering oar.

lands. Without a compass this was a truly hazardous
undertaking, even for seamen as skilled as the Vikings. It
is now thought that they were the first Europeans to have
landed on the American continent.

Ships of the Middle Ages were often pictured on seals,
carvings and tapestries; one of the most famous of the
latter is the Bayeux tapestry on which is pictured the
Mora, William the Conqueror's ship (eleventh century).
In many respects it was very like the Viking long ships.
By the thirteenth century—if the evidence of port seals
can be relied on—sea-going ships had gone over from
oars to sails for power, and turreted castles began to
appear fore and aft.

One of the strongest and most urgent influences on
ship design during this period was the Crusades. The
great problem of the shipbuilders of those times was to
construct ships large enough to carry the thousands of
soldiers and pilgrims—and their masses of goods and
chattels—going out to fight the heretics and heathens.
These ships also had to bring back loads of loot, since,
for some nobles at least, the Crusades had very material
ends. Other developments during the Middle Ages—not
all arising from the Crusades—included the introduction
of the stern-rudder and tiller, the carrying of both square
and lateen sails by two-masted vessels and the vastly
enlarged bulwarks.

Interestingly, the terms "starboard" and "port" were
derived from the days when ships were steered by a
single rudder-oar. This was always positioned on the
right-hand side of a vessel, which was thus called the

14

"steering side," and later the "starboard" side. As it was unsafe to bring a ship into port with the rudder-oar against the dock, for fear of damaging it, a ship was always berthed with its left side against the dock and this side became known as the "port" side.

By the end of the thirteenth century, all was set for the great advances of the Renaissance, which began in the fourteenth century and laid the foundations of modern ship design and the adventurous exploration and exploitation of the whole world.

A war galley of the 16th century. The advantage of this type of craft was that it was faster than the galeasse and did not have to rely on the wind. Galleys played a leading role in the Battle of Lepanto (1571).

A mariner's compass. This type was used in the 17th century.

the great age of sail

The Renaissance which began in Italy in the fourteenth century was a period in which man moved forward in the fields of learning and art as perhaps never before. It was also a period when he opened his eyes to the material possibilities of the whole world, not, as before, concentrating only on the regions of the Mediterranean and eastern Atlantic.

As we have seen, during the thirteenth and fourteenth centuries ship builders had started to construct ships which were capable of sailing any of the great oceans. This was not possible, however, until the introduction of the magnetic compass in the fifteenth century and the development of the method of sailing known as "tacking." Tacking enables a ship to move forward regardless of the direction of the wind by zig-

An engraving of Columbus landing on Watling Island, 1492. The ship in the foreground is the *Santa Maria*, Columbus' flagship.

An East Indiaman (seventeenth century).
These craft were armed and used on the East India run.

zagging from one side to the other, trimming the sails to catch the wind from whatever direction it is blowing.

It is hard to understand today how mysterious the world was for men five hundred years ago. They knew only their little bit of the earth. They had, it is true, travelled to India and the Far East along the seaways and the caravan routes of the ancient world. But most of the lands and seas south and west of the Mediterranean were as unknown to them as the planet Mars is to us—perhaps more so.

What was beyond the western rim of the Atlantic, where "The Sea of Darkness," as they called it, rolled far away towards the sunset? The Vikings may have touched the far land of America, but they had little

A Baltimore clipper (late eighteenth century). Their
fine lines represent an outstanding advance in ship design.

idea of where they had been. Had Christopher Columbus known more
about this unknown world, he would never have set off on his westward
voyage. For years he had dreamed of sailing west and reaching Asia by
going partly round the world. Many people opposed Columbus' idea;
they understood better than he how big the world was, and they pointed
out that in the small, slow ships of the day his crews would die of hunger
and thirst long before they reached Asia. But Columbus insisted that the
distance between the Canary Islands and Japan was only 2,400 miles, or
less than a quarter of what it actually is. And so persuasive was this
austere seaman that the King and Queen of Spain provided him with
three vessels and men for the expedition. Thus it was that at sunset on

An American clipper getting under way.
This craft was designed about 1840
and built by New England shipbuilders.

20

October 11, 1492, thirty-one days after leaving the Canaries, Columbus'
ships, *Nina, Pinta* and *Santa Maria,* the flagship, were running on a
westerly course before a gale in an unknown sea. Then, soon after 2:00
A.M. the next morning, the moon illuminated dimly, not Japan, but an
unknown island in a yet unnamed sea. With daylight Columbus landed,
naming the place San Salvador. It was what we now know as Watling
Island, in the Bahamas. Following this voyage, Columbus made three
others. The last one ended in failure, and he died unhonoured and
neglected.

Other fifteenth century men also became curious about the
unexplored places of the world. Gradually, in the course of many
expeditions, ships worked their way down the west coast of Africa to
lands where gold and ivory might be traded. The Cape of Good Hope
was rounded. But still no sea route to the great lands of India had been
discovered. This was the achievement of Vasco Da Gama and the
Portuguese. The Da Gama expedition of 1497 was well equipped with
the best ships that could be designed for the purpose. After calling at the

A spritsail sailing barge. These elegant vessels were
used as cargo carriers on the River Thames but are now,
regrettably, almost all replaced by power-driven ships.

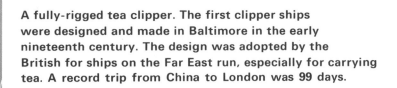

A fully-rigged tea clipper. The first clipper ships were designed and made in Baltimore in the early nineteenth century. The design was adopted by the British for ships on the Far East run, especially for carrying tea. A record trip from China to London was 99 days.

Cape Verde Islands, Da Gama sailed not due south, but far out to the westward into the Atlantic where better winds might be picked up, and only when he was south of Brazil and a few hundred miles from it, did he turn east, eventually reaching the African coast a little north of Cape Town. The voyage from the Cape Verde Islands alone entailed more than three months at sea. The expedition rounded the Cape of Good Hope in bad weather and worked up the east African coast. The crews developed scurvy, a disease produced by lack of green vegetables. All the early mariners suffered from scurvy on long voyages and many died of it. Eventually Da Gama's ships reached as far north as Malindi. From there they headed off again across the Indian Ocean. Once more the squadron was on the broad back of an ocean, and even with the south-west monsoon from astern to blow them to India, three weeks at sea passed before they dropped their anchors and went ashore at Calicut. The sea route to India had been found.

Twenty-five years later, on September 8, 1522, a galleon of about seventy-five feet in length, having eighteen white men and four natives of the Spice Islands on board, dropped anchor in the Guadalquivir river in the Spanish province of Seville. She was the *Vittoria*, and she and her crew of eighteen were all that was left of a squadron of five ships, carrying two hundred and seventy-five men, that had sailed from the same river three years earlier. The *Vittoria* was the first ship to spread her sails in the great spaces of the Pacific and sail all the way round the world. Ferdinand Magellan, the commander of the expedition, was among the many who died on the great voyage.

The voyage had been dogged by hunger verging on starvation, and by scurvy. Like Columbus, Magellan had put into the Canaries for stores. Unknown to him, however, the full amount was not loaded. The ships then sailed southwest, along the coast of South America, putting in at Rio, the River Plate, and St. Julian's Bay. Already there were signs of trouble in the squadron. Magellan quelled a mutiny, beheading one of his ship's captains. Later a vessel of the squadron was wrecked, another ship deserted, and eventually only three ships passed through the strait now called Magellan.

Now they found themselves on the Pacific; and over this empty world of water they sailed on in fair winds for almost three months. By the end of this time they were eating leather from the anti-chafing gear between the yards and the masts. It was a voyage that none of them, not even Magellan himself, would have undertaken had they known the vastness of the empty sea between South America and Guam Island, in the western Pacific, which they eventually reached. Later they sailed on to the Philippines, where Magellan was killed in a battle with the natives. Here, too, one of the ships was abandoned after the transfer of crew and stores. Soon after, another one was left behind, its condition having become dangerous after such long and hard service. One ship now sailed on, the *Vittoria* commanded by Del Camo. Eventually, it rounded the Cape of Good Hope and sailed up the south Atlantic to Spain. The voyage was over. The world had been circumnavigated, and, in addition, Magellan had proved that America was a separate continent and not part of Asia.

This was an age of great and daring seamen and two of the greatest were John Cabot and Amerigo Vespucci. John Cabot led an English expedition for Henry VII and discovered (1497) part of the North American mainland; it was on this that the English based their claims on North America. Amerigo Vespucci was an Italian who made several transatlantic voyages, exploring the mouth of the Amazon river in 1499. The continent was named after him in the erroneous belief that he was the first European to land on the American mainland.

The oceans became freeways across which ships could travel and engage in trade on a truly international scale. From the seventeenth to nineteenth centuries the merchant ships were in the main adaptions of pinnaces and frigates. One successful type of merchant ship was the "East Indiaman," built by the Dutch for trading with the East Indies, a Dutch Colony. These ships were satisfactory so far as their capacity to carry cargoes was concerned. As competition among ship owners increased, they became more concerned with speed, and it was this concern that led to the development of a class of ship which was not only fast but one of the most elegant ships ever sailed, the clipper.

The clipper was developed from the schooner, which itself came from the cutter. Clippers reached the peak of their development in America during the nineteenth century. The best known was the "Baltimore" clipper, a sleek sharp-bowed vessel. The first real clipper was the *Rainbow* built in New York in 1845. It was 154 feet long and had a beam of $31\frac{1}{2}$ feet. The largest clipper—one of the largest wooden ships ever built—was the four-masted *Great Republic*, which was 325 feet long and 53 feet wide. The fastest clipper was undoubtedly the *Flying Cloud* which could cover over 370 sea miles a day on a good run. Another famous clipper was the *Cutty Sark*, still to be seen at Greenwich, London. She is 212 feet long, 36 feet wide and has a net tonnage of 920, and was specially built for bringing tea from China.

These sailing greyhounds were wonderfully fast. For example, in May 1866 two tea clippers, the *Ariel* and *Taeping*, competing for a substantial prize and bonus, raced from the port of Foochow to London dock. The two ships docked on the same tide, having covered the 15,000 mile journey in 99 days.

An effort was made during the first twenty-five years of the present century to keep sail alive on the ocean trade routes. For this purpose, huge multi-masted schooners were built. Among them were some of the biggest sailing vessels ever to appear. They had one great advantage over the clipper ship: their rig was easily handled by fewer men. They also were designed to take heavy loads of the kinds of cargo that did not need to be carried too quickly and would profit from the economy offered by sail.

Among these big schooners was the largest wooden sailing vessel ever built, the *Wyoming* of 1910, which had six masts. Many of the schooners carried more masts than had ever been used previously in sailing vessels.

26

Four masts were common. There were five-masters and six-masters, and even one seven-master, the *Thomas W. Lawson*, a steel vessel built in 1902. A number of large schooners were built during the 1914–18 war and, from the point of view of economy, were able to compete with steamers. After the war a German firm built a class of five-masted sailing ships with an unusual rig which included fore-and-aft and square·sails.

These schooners and the similarly rigged ships had deck machinery for hoisting and handling the sails, and for all other heavy work. They also had powerful auxiliary engines so that they might be kept moving in calms. These ships represented the last efforts to make sail compete profitably with steamships, and in some measure they succeeded. Big vessels though they were, they could be manned by a crew of no more than a dozen hands, while carrying 5,000 tons of cargo.

In this mechanical age, the ultimate failure of sailing ships was inevitable. But there are a few areas in the world where sailing vessels still work. Some of them are to be found today in the Grand Banks Fisheries.

An early American whaler
going into action. At that
time sperm and right whales were
hunted for their oil, which
was used in making
fuel for lamps,
candles and ointments.

The life of a sailor on a whaler
was tough and dangerous.
The small boat which carried
the harpoonist was easily
smashed by the threshing
tail of a desperate whale.

The Portuguese and certain French Grand Banks schooners also have auxiliary engines, which give them a reasonable speed when the wind is light. The advantage of using sail for these ships is that they have to make a long voyage to and from the fishing grounds, and spend a long period of time on the grounds. Without sail they would have to carry excessive quantities of fuel. This is the kind of condition under which sail may still be of value and produce some of the loveliest ships afloat. Such is the four-masted auxiliary schooner *Argus*, a steel vessel of 177 feet in length, able to carry six hundred tons of salted fish back from the fishing grounds. Built in Holland for Portuguese owners in 1939, this great vessel, with her graceful hull and lovely lines, seems to belong to an earlier age of seafaring. She carries seventy-two fishermen and yet may be handled by a crew of only nine. One of the few examples of contemporary working sailing ships embodying the most modern ideas in design and construction, she represents an unbroken line of descent from earlier generations of sailing vessels intended for the same work.

Those areas of the world that are commonly known as under-developed are where working sailing craft may still be found in the greatest number, though they are steadily decreasing. They are also found in a few localities which, if not backward, are sufficiently non-industrial to provide sail with a value that busier societies can no longer find for it. Sailing ships are still used in the West Indies, for example, where schooners and smaller sailing craft carry fruit and passengers from one to another of the islands.

In Europe, sail propulsion began its long history in the Mediterranean, as we have already seen. The windlessness of the Mediterranean, however, is discouraging for sail. In the past the oared galley was used to propel the ship during the long calms, and today auxiliary engines are used for the same purpose, in even the simplest craft. But a few fully equipped sailing craft are still to be found. Arab schooners run along the Syrian and Palestinian coast, from Egypt to Alexandretta, the port of Aleppo. This famous stretch of coast runs due north and south, while the prevailing wind is northerly; so the schooners have to spend much of their time beating against head winds. As a result they have developed

**The *Danmark* fully rigged, setting
out on the Sailtraining Race from Oslo to Ostend.**

almost yacht-like rigs with triangular main and foresails. They have a
dashing air, with the masts heavily raked and the foremast in the eyes
of the ships. The main boom overhangs the stern by half its length,
while the foresail, which is without a boom, overlaps the mainsail, and
the ships carry long bow-sprits. In this way, as much sail as possible is
crowded above the hull. But ships like these are no longer being built.

In the nearby Aegean Sea, luggers are to be seen under sail, with
graceful curved yards aslant on the masts, and jibs set from a long bowsprit. But though the sails are used regularly, an auxiliary engine is

A sea-going junk.

fitted inside the hull. Elsewhere in this part of the world sailing craft will come into view from time to time. It may be a lateen rigged felucca, with its sail cutting across the sky like an oriental curved sword above the banks of the Nile, whose waters have carried vessels hardly distinguishable from her since the days when sail was young. Many sailing craft are like that—they have changed little with time, and you may still discover in odd places the oldest kinds of ships still afloat and working.

No ship reveals this more clearly than the Chinese junk. There are scholars who suggest that the art of using sail originated in China. They believe that the junk is the father of all rigs, and that its example spread westward, eventually to the Mediterranean and the Egyptians, in the course of many changes. This may or may not be the case. The junk is certainly very old and has been altered little with the passing of centuries. And there she is still, crossing the China Sea, where squalls come like puffs from an oven to herald a typhoon, or navigating far inland in China's thousands of miles of rivers.

It seems a long way from the junk to the modern yacht. About fifty years ago it was usually thought that the sailing yacht, like most of the working craft of sail, would soon be extinct, its place taken by the motor yachts and boats that were appearing then for the first time. This has not happened. Perhaps the reason is that as the automobile has ceased to give pleasure, the sailing boat remains the last refuge of travel freedom. Alone among all types of sailing vessels, sailing yachts are now more numerous than ever before. They are heirs of all sailing vessels, the last and most advanced achievements in sail propulsion, and we will learn more about them in the chapter called "Boats for Pleasure."

31

A river trading junk.

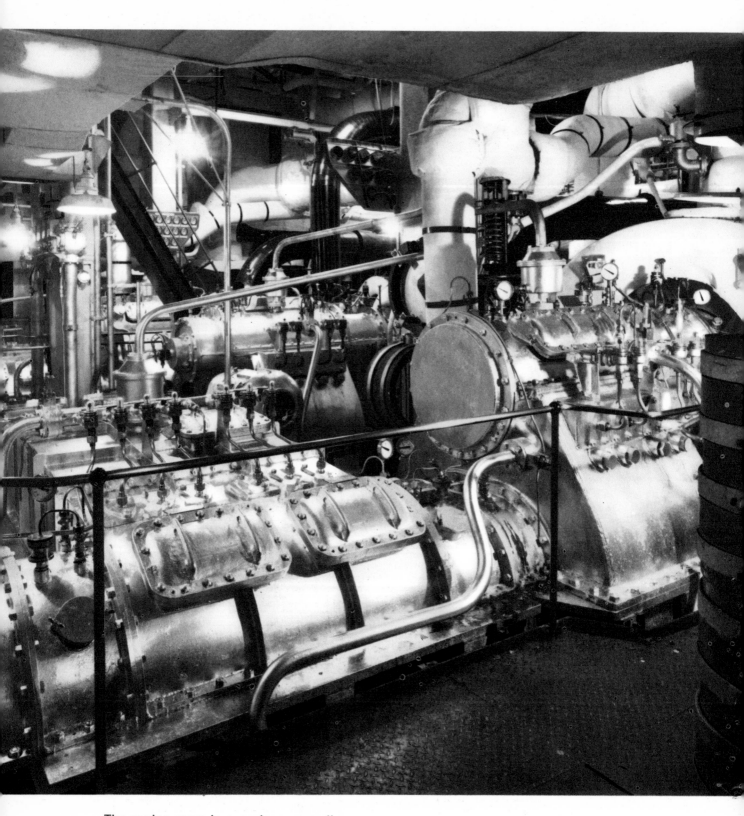

The engine-room in a modern ocean liner.

The *Charlotte Dundas*, built in 1801.
It was used to tow barges on the
Forth and Clyde Canal and was
powered by a 10 horse-power engine.

power for ships

James Watt and the other men who pioneered the development of the steam engine started just as great a revolution in sea transport as they did in railways. One of the first attempts to apply the steam engine to a ship was made around 1715 by a group of French marine engineers who used one of James Watt's engines, but like so many marine pioneers before them, they could not convince the authorities that this new advance would be of any service to the French nation, and so their work went for nothing. Jonathan Hulls, an Englishman, experimented with model steam ships but though he was granted a patent by George II, he could not raise sufficient money to build an actual ship. In 1786, John Fitch, an American engineer, constructed a steamboat with two banks of vertical oars which produced a speed of about 3 miles per hour. About the same time James Rumsey, another American marine engineer, built a boat powered by a pump. In this vessel, the steam-operated pump

Robert Fulton's *Clermont*, built in 1807.
She ran between New York and Albany
and after some changes was renamed *North River*.

34 was used to suck in water at the bows and expel it at the stern—the first example of a jet-propelled ship!

Perhaps the first real step forward was the *Charlotte Dundas*, built by William Symington in 1801. It was propelled by a paddle wheel housed in the hull and was used as a tug-boat on the Forth–Clyde Canal. In 1807 Robert Fulton built the *Clermont*, a paddle steamer which was fitted with a Boulton and Watt engine. She plied between New York and Albany and after modifications was re-christened *North River*. The paddle steamer *Comet* was built in 1812 by Henry Bell and operated a service on the river Clyde. This ship was the first steamship service to run in Europe and can be said to have founded the steamship industry.

When the steam engine had proved it could be successfully employed to drive ships, progress was fast and diverse. In 1818 Moses Rogers constructed the first real ocean-going vessel, the *Savannah*, which set sail from New York for Liverpool on May 22, 1819. Since the voyage was essentially a trial run, the *Savannah* carried no passengers or cargo. The trial was partially successful, although it should be noted that only a part of the voyage was completed under steam power because fuel ran out before the ship reached port. The voyage took $29\frac{1}{2}$ days. The

Although the paddle steamer *Savannah*
was the first steam-propelled vessel
to cross the Atlantic, it was
Sirius, pictured above, which introduced
the first regular service in 1838. She
was 703 tons and carried 100 passengers
on her first voyage.

The steamship *Great Britain* designed
by Isambard Kingdom Brunel. She is
important in the history of ships in
being propeller driven and constructed
of iron. She was 322 feet long with
a beam of 51 feet and an estimated
3,448 tons. She made an average speed
of 12 knots with a six-bladed propeller.

The *Royal William* (1838).

Braemar Castle (1872).

The *Algeria* (1869).

problem of the large amount of fuel needed to stoke the boilers was one of the reasons why shipping interests were slow to accept the steam-powered vessel. Their concern was carrying as much cargo as possible —not fuel.

Another problem in these early sea-going vessels was that they used paddle wheels. These were reasonably efficient for inland waterways and offshore sailing, but in waves and heavy swell they lifted out of the water and became useless as a means of propulsion. One of the most impressive of all the many designs of paddle steamer was the Mississippi river boats. This was a flat-bottomed craft with the engine on the main

The steamship *City of New York*, 1888.

deck, powering two large paddles on either side of the vessel or a single paddle wheel at the stern. A classic example of this strikingly majestic vessel was the *Memphis* built in 1852. She was a giant by any standards, with three decks, all ornately decorated and furnished.

In spite of the achievement of the *Savannah* it took another 20 years before the steam engine was fully accepted. Acceptance was hastened greatly by the successful voyages of the *Sirius* (703 tons) and the *Great Western* (1,340 tons). The *Great Western* was a product of the English engineering genius Isambard Kingdom Brunel, who also designed the first iron ships, the *Great Britain* (3,448 tons) and the *Great Eastern*. The

The *Great Eastern* was a giant with a gross tonnage of 18,914,
692 feet long and an 82 feet beam. Great things were expected
of her but she ended her days by laying the first Atlantic cable.

Great Britain was the first screw vessel to cross the Atlantic. The *Great Eastern* was one of the key ships of history and one of its greatest white elephants. The *Great Eastern* was specifically designed to prove the advantages of iron construction and the feasibility of carrying great numbers of passengers and great amounts of cargo. She was 18,918 tons, 692 feet long and had accommodation for some 4,000 passengers! Propelled by paddle wheels and screw-propellers, she was powered by steam engines developing 6,600 horsepower. Her performance as a passenger-cargo vessel was a dismal failure and she was later put to use as a cable-layer, a job at which she was very successful.

The screw propeller based on the Archimedean water-screw was invented simultaneously by Francis P. Smith and John Ericsson, and the first ship to be fitted with a screw was the appropriately named *Archimedes* in 1838. The peak of nineteenth century steamships were the Cunard liners *Lucania* and *Campania* (1893), which were built of steel and fitted with steam engines generating 30,000 horsepower.

39

The very first engines used in ships were dangerous, dirty and above all not very efficient. The basic design is what is known as a reciprocating engine. In improved models, this is still used in many ships to this day. It consists of a number of cylinders placed upright over the crankshaft which in turn is connected to the propeller shaft. Steam from the boilers is admitted into the cylinder through a valve, expands, forces the piston down, and this revolves the crankshaft. In general construction this engine is similar to the internal combustion engine used in automobiles.

The earliest boilers were made of iron or copper which

40

could not withstand high pressures without blowing up. For this reason the low pressure steam produced was often divided between two cylinders, both working at the same pressure. With stronger boilers higher pressures became possible. It soon became apparent that the steam still possessed a large amount of energy after it had been used, and this led to a new development, which was to pass on steam that had been used in one cylinder to another one of lower pressure. This type of engine is known as the compound engine. With advances in boiler design it was safe to produce high steam pressures and hence greater power for less fuel. Out of this followed the triple and then the

quadruple expansion engines. It is the triple expansion engine which is most widely used today. As its name suggests, the steam is used in three stages—high, intermediate and low. The quadruple expansion engine is not very widely used as it is somewhat complicated.

One of the most important advances in marine power was Sir Charles Parsons' steam turbine, patented in 1884 and originally designed to drive dynamos that generated electric power. Compared to the steam engine, the turbine was far more compact and efficient. To show how much better steam turbines were, Parsons built a boat, the *Turbinia*, powered by three turbines developing some 2,000 horse-power and driving nine propellers. To convince the British Admiralty, traditionally slow to accept new ideas, Parsons sailed it at the Jubilee Naval Review in 1897, where it achieved the then incredible speed of $34\frac{1}{2}$ knots.

The steam turbine works on the same principle as the windmill. In the turbine the windmill is replaced by a rotor made up of thousands of slightly curved blades. When the high-pressure steam strikes the blades the rotor shaft turns. One of the disadvantages—if it can be really considered one—is the fact that the turbine must run at very high speeds to work at peak efficiency. If the rotor shaft was coupled directly to the propeller shaft, it would turn the propellers very rapidly, thus churning up the water so violently that the propellers would have no water to bite into. Usually, therefore, the rotor shaft is coupled to the propeller shaft through a gearing stage which reduces the propeller speed to around 100 revolutions per minute.

The first passenger ship to incorporate a steam turbine was the *King Edward* (1901), a Clyde River packet, and in six or seven years the turbine was being used in Atlantic liners. The first of these, the *Victorian* of 10,635 tons, had a top speed of 19 knots. This ship was the first of the Atlantic "greyhounds," fast luxury liners. The best-known of these, each designed to carry over 2,000 passengers, were the *Mauretania* and the ill-fated *Lusitania*, which was sunk by a German submarine in 1915 with a loss of 1,198 lives.

At about the same time that Charles Parsons was developing the steam turbine, Rudolf Diesel, a German inventor, was perfecting his oil engine—now commonly known as the diesel engine. The first sea-going diesel-powered ship was the *Selandia*, built in 1912. In the main diesel-powered vessels, which are often called "motor ships," have been developed for the merchant navy. It was predicted that diesel engines would replace steam in

Turbinia, the first ship to be powered by a steam
turbine. She is seen here steaming at the amazing speed
of 34 knots at the Diamond Jubilee Naval Review in 1897.

The paddle steamer *Duchess of Rothesay*. Steamers of this type were widely used all over the world for short journeys.

A Mississippi river steamboat. Perhaps the most magnificent of these splendid boats was the *Natchez* and the fastest the *Robert E. Lee* which did the journey from New Orleans to St. Louis in under four days.

marine vessels but this has not as yet happened, in spite of the diesel's
greater fuel efficiency and the much smaller engine-room space it
demands.

Unlike the internal combustion engine, the charge in a diesel engine
is not fired by an electric spark. Instead, the diesel takes advantage of the
fact that when air is compressed it becomes very hot. The upward stroke
of the piston raises the temperature of the air in the diesel cylinder.
When atomized fuel oil is squirted into this hot air, it burns. This forces
the piston down, and the downward movement of the piston turns the
crankshaft in much the same way as it does in a steam engine. Although
there are many designs of marine oil engine, they all work on the same
principle.

One commonly used design—originally designed for tramp ships—
has two pistons in each cylinder and the combustion takes place between
them, forcing one up and the other down. Diesel engines, like racing-car
engines, can be supercharged to increase their power. Diesel engines
are usually coupled directly to the propeller shaft so that it runs at the
same speed as the engine. There is no problem here, except that a very
big and heavy engine is required to withstand the strain. To reduce

engine size, some ships are fitted with high-speed oil engines that are geared to the propeller shaft in the same way that the steam turbine is. This set-up allows for smaller and lighter engines. It is also possible to gear two or even four engines to the same propeller shaft and secure the same power with a much smaller engine room, which means there is more room for cargo. It also means that one engine can be shut down for running repairs or service without making too much difference in the speed of the vessel.

Perhaps the ultimate in power is nuclear energy. Too often we are reminded of its destructive features, but it has a great positive value, and soon after the Second World War it was applied to ship propulsion. This was as important a development for man's command of the sea as the jump from sail to steam. The nuclear engine is a reactor in which the radioactive element, Uranium 235, breaks down by a process known as fission and generates a great quantity of heat in the process. It is this heat which is used to drive steam turbines in exactly the same way as the traditional steam engine. The great advantage of nuclear power is the economy in fuel, which gives the ship greater capacity for passengers and cargo, as well as increased speeds.

The *Canberra*, one of the most up-to-date passenger liners, has a striking streamlined form with side-by-side funnels placed close to the stern. She is 820 feet overall, has a 102 feet beam and a gross tonnage of 45,000. The *Canberra* is powered by oil-fired steam turbines driving electric motors coupled to twin propellers. These develop 85,000 horse power to give an average speed of 27 knots.

48

A U.S. ballistic-missile nuclear submarine about to submerge. Once
down she may not break surface for more than two months.

A Greek fighting galley of the 4th century B.C.

fighting ships

The Greeks, Romans and Phoenicians all used warships different in design and construction from their trading vessels. The early Greek warships had a kind of tower amidships which afforded good observation and a strong pointed ram built into the bows. At the height of its power, the Greek navy used biremes that were more than sixty feet long and had fifty to sixty oarsmen. The Romans probably used triremes as fighting vessels, and these had a tower amidships which afforded a good position for fighting.

It was at the time of the Crusades, in the thirteenth century, that fighting ships from northern Europe sailed down to the Mediterranean and across it to attack the Saracens in the Holy Land. These vessels were similar in general design to the Viking ships, and it seems likely that they were mainly sailing vessels that used oars only when they were becalmed. At this time castle-like structures began to appear in the bow and at the stern of these ships. So far as we know at present, there were

A Crusader ship
of the thirteenth century
with lateen sails.

The *Henry Grâce à Dieu* or the *Great Harry*, built by Henry VIII in 1514. She was about 1,000 tons and carried 21 heavy guns and 130 iron guns.

no other significant changes in the design of fighting ships in the fourteenth century.

By the end of the fifteenth century, warships had begun to show considerable advances in shipbuilding and design. They became much bigger vessels, possibly 125 feet long and 34 feet wide, carried three masts and, for the first time, a number of guns. These ships were known as carracks.

It was in the sixteenth century that the galleon came to be used as a warship. One of the biggest and best-known warships of this period was the *Henry Grâce à Dieu*—usually called the Great Harry—which was first built in 1514 and completely rebuilt between 1536–39. She was flat-sterned and had an enormous forecastle which projected out over her bows. She had six decks astern and carried 21 heavy bronze guns, 130 iron guns and 100 smaller hand guns. Like other ships of this period she had a heavy grapnel on her bowsprit which was used to hold other ships at close quarters while fighting. This famous warship belonged to the fleet of Henry VIII of England.

Nelson's flagship *Victory*. She was 226 feet long with a 51-feet beam. She carried a total of 102 guns and a crew of 850. She is now at Portsmouth.

The Battle of Lepanto(1571) was one of the greatest naval battles in history. It was fought between the Turks and the combined fleets of Spain, Venice, the Pope and Malta.

In spite of the increasing use of sails, many ships still had oars as well. These were known as galeasses, and they played a great part in the battle of Lepanto in 1571 when Spain, Malta and Italy conquered the Turkish fleet of galleys.

During the seventeenth century there was little change in the design of fighting ships, and the galleons and galeasses which had fought in the great battles between England and the Spanish Armada continued to dominate the seas. This was true until the eighteenth century, when the frigate came into use as a warship.

Frigates were strong, fast ships which carried between 30 and 40 guns all mounted on the same deck. The most famous of all first-raters and of all fighting ships as well was Nelson's flagship *Victory*, which he commanded at the battle of Trafalgar in 1805. *Victory* has been preserved as it was originally and is on view in dry dock at Portsmouth today. She was built at Chatham between 1759–65, but was rebuilt before she

52

British fleet in action off Carthagena, a Spanish fortified port, in 1708.

was used at Trafalgar. She is 226 feet long and 51·5 feet wide, and at Trafalgar she carried 102 guns and a crew of 850 men. The largest frigates ever to be built were *United States*, *President* and *Constitution*, which entered the service of the American navy in 1800. They were 204 feet long, 44·3 feet wide, and carried 54 guns.

The change from wooden fighting ships to ones built of metal began in 1859, when the first metal-protected ship, the French frigate *Gloire*, was launched in 1859. She was built of wood but was protected along her waterline and over part of the hull by 5-inch thick metal plating. She weighed 5,675 tons and achieved speeds of up to 13 knots. She was 252·5 feet long, 55 feet wide, and had a draught of 25 feet. In 1860 the British launched the frigate *Warrior*, which was built completely of iron. She was not unlike the swift clippers except that she was powered by a screw propeller turned by a steam engine generating 1,250 horse power. Her average speed was about 14 knots.

53

The Battle of Trafalgar, a cape on the Atlantic coast of Spain, where Nelson defeated the combined fleets of France and Spain in 1805.

The battle of the first ironclads at Hampton Roads in
March 1862. *Left*, *Monitor*, armed with two 11-inch guns
in a rotating iron turret, and *right*, *Merrimac*, whose
gun deck was metal-plated. She probably carried ten guns.

The *Warrior* was one of the first steam-driven warships, and by the
time of the Crimean War in 1853, most naval men were convinced of
the superiority of warships that used steam power. One early and
peculiar steam-driven warship appeared in 1862 during the American
Civil War. This was the Southern ship called the *Merrimac*, an old
steam-screw frigate which had been sunk by the Union troops, then
salvaged and patched up. The *Merrimac* had no masts, sat very low in
the water, and was topped by a superstructure of wood and iron two
feet thick. She carried ten guns. To oppose the *Merrimac* the Union
forces had the *Monitor*, another strange ship, designed by Swedish
engineer John Ericsson. The hull consisted of two parts: an underwater
body 124 feet long, 34 feet wide and 5·8 feet deep; and above this a

The Russian circular battleship
Novgorod. Designed by Admiral Popoff,
it was of about 2,500 tons and
carried two 11-inch guns.

larger hull 175 feet long, 41·5 feet wide and 5 feet high. Only about 3 feet of the hull appeared above water. The *Monitor* had a rotating gun tower amidships with two guns. Astern of this were two removable funnels and two removable ventilation shafts. The *Monitor* succeeded in sinking the *Merrimac*, but was herself close to sinking after the engagement.

In the latter part of the nineteenth century in Europe bigger and stronger warships were built to carry larger, more powerful guns. The British *Royal Sovereign* of 1892 was 380 feet long, 75 feet deep and displaced 14,150 tons. She had higher sides than was usual in battleship construction to lessen the slowing effect of waves breaking over the decks. *Royal Sovereign* had four $13\frac{1}{2}$-inch guns and many lighter guns, and could reach speeds of 18 knots. The French and German battleships of the same period were much heavier vessels, like huge fortresses. Typical examples of these naval dinosaurs were the French *Charles-Martel* of 1893, which was protected at the waterline with steel plating 18 inches thick, and the German *Kaiser Barbarossa* (1900), which was heavily plated and equally heavily armed—she carried 38 guns and was equipped with five torpedo tubes.

56

The first warship to be driven by turbine engines and to have many large caliber guns which enabled her to fire salvoes of shots over long distances was the *Dreadnought*, launched in 1906. *Dreadnought* displaced 17,900 tons and had ten 12-inch guns and heavy steel plating. She was fast, achieving a speed of 21 knots, and very effective. Her design became the basis for the battleships of all the western nations for many

The U.S. battleship *Idaho*.

The American aircraft carrier *Lexington* (1925). She could carry
about 90 planes and a crew of 1,780, and speed at 34½ knots.

years. The United States built similar battleships like the 27,400-ton
Texas and the *New York*.

During World War I, battleships became larger and more heavily
armed, a trend that culminated in the British battleship *Hood,* which was
completed too late for the First World War and was sunk by German
ships in the Second. She displaced 41,200 tons, had eight 15-inch guns

57

The British battle-cruiser *Hood*. She was armed with eight
15-inch guns and was one of the largest ships of her time (1920).
The *Hood* had 144,000 horse-power engines and could speed at 31 knots.

and many smaller guns.

Following World War I, a movement for naval disarmament developed. At the Washington Conference of 1922, the leading navies of the world were banned from building battleships larger than 35,000 tons or having guns of more than 15 inch caliber. Germany was not allowed ships over 10,000 tons. To get around this restriction, Germany built "pocket battleships" like the *Deutschland* and the *Admiral Graf Spee*, which were fast enough to run from battleships and had sufficient armament to defeat the smaller cruisers. When Hitler came to power, he ignored all restrictions and went ahead with the building of such capital ships as the *Scharnhorst, Bismarck* and *Tirpitz*; the last two were over 52,000 tons displacement and carried eight 15-inch guns.

The Second World War proved that battleships were too slow at turning and consequently too open and expensive as targets, and aircraft carriers replaced them as the largest unit in navies. The first aircraft carrier in the modern sense was the *Furious*, which was converted from a cruiser and had a rather short flight deck. The *Lexington* and *Saratoga* of the U.S. Navy were the most expensive fighting ships of their time. They displaced 33,000 tons, could achieve speeds of $34\frac{1}{2}$ knots, and could carry 90 planes. The U.S. carrier *Forrestal* is the largest warship in the world driven by conventional power. It has an angled flight deck and catapult launching and catching gear. The *Forrestal* can carry 90 to 100 planes and reach a speed of 34 knots. The latest advance in the design of aircraft carriers is the American nuclear-

Preparing to launch a "Phantom" fighter-bomber from the *Enterprise*.

The U.S. carrier *Forrestal* which can steam at
34 knots and carry 90 to 100 planes and a crew of 3,400 men.

powered *Enterprise*. She is 1,100 feet long, has a flight deck 2 2 feet long
and displaces 85,000 tons.

In both World Wars I and II the cruiser played an important part in
sea battles for the simple reason that it was lighter and faster than the
battleship. Some earlier cruisers were completely steel-plated but this
added Steel weight reduced their speed. Consequently the so-called
light cruiser, like the British Navy's *Sheffield*, became the most common

type. *Sheffield* was 591 feet long, 64 feet wide and had a draught of 21 feet. She had 4-inch-thick plates at the waterline amidships and carried nine 6-inch guns, eight 4-inch, 40 anti-aircraft guns and six torpedo tubes. The American cruiser *Boston*, built in 1955, was the first to be equipped with anti-aircraft guided missiles. The first nuclear-powered cruiser to carry guided missiles, the *Long Beach*, can counter attacks from any type of ship or aircraft armed with conventional or nuclear weapons.

Smaller than cruisers, destroyers are fast ships with only small guns on deck, but fitted with torpedoes, which were first used in the American Civil War. The modern British destroyers of the "Daring" class are 390 feet long, 43 feet wide and displace 3,600 tons. They have a top speed of about 35 knots and carry six $4\frac{1}{2}$-inch guns, five torpedo tubes and many other anti-submarine weapons. Larger destroyers which carry guided missiles have recently been built, and the American destroyer *Bainbridge* is nuclear-powered.

The smallest of the modern fighting ships are the torpedo boats, which can reach speeds of between 40 and 50 knots and carry torpedoes and machine guns. They are usually about 40 feet long and powered with jet engines similar to those used in aircraft.

Two other kinds of fighting ships, corvettes and frigates, were developed as submarine-hunting vessels. They had listening devices for tracking submarines, and their main armament was depth charges. Many frigates nowadays are equipped like destroyers, and some also carry helicopters to help them in submarine hunting.

Mine warfare at sea played an important role in the two World Wars, and special ships were developed to lay and detect mines. Many mine-layers are converted from other classes to perform the task, but one of the largest minelayers, the U.S. *Terror*, was specially built. She is 453 feet long and can carry 800 mines, and has four 5-inch guns and nine anti-aircraft guns. Mine sweeping for impact mines is an operation similar to trawler fishing; the mines are collected in a net and disarmed. Magnetic and acoustic mines need special sweeping techniques, and modern minesweepers carry a variety of equipment for dealing with different types of mines.

Another specialized naval craft that was important in World War II

Helicopters landing on the deck
of an aircraft carrier. These
machines are now playing an
important role in the navy,
not only as air-sea rescue craft
but as submarine hunters and transports.

Right, a missile destroyer firing
a guided missile. This class of ship
is being rapidly developed by the
world's leading navies. Some of the
new models are nuclear powered.
The American *Long Beach* carries
guided missiles in addition to
torpedoes and anti-submarine guns.

An assault ship and landing
craft. These can work close
to shore, taking combat troops
directly to assault landings.

was the landing craft used to carry troops and tanks in to shore. They played an outstanding role in the War in the Pacific and in the landing at Normandy.

The major naval vessel in both World War I and II was the submarine. The idea of the submarine was first suggested in 1578 but never built. In 1775 David Bushnell, an American engineer, built the first practical submarine, the *Turtle*, which rather resembled its name. The first naval submarine was built in 1775 and many experiments with different designs were carried out until the beginning of World War I, when submarines were first readily accepted as fighting vessels. Since about 1890, submarines have been built with pressure hulls containing all the vital equipment, and ballast tanks for diving and surfacing outside this hull. They carry deck guns for fighting on the surface and torpedo tubes for use underwater.

Modern nuclear-powered submarines like the American *Nautilus* are an important development in submarine warfare. *Nautilus* is capable of 21 knots and can travel 40,000 nautical miles before refueling. She has traveled to the North Pole under the Arctic ice cap. Britain's first nuclear-powered submarine was the *Dreadnought*. Nuclear-powered submarines can launch guided missiles armed with an atomic warhead from underwater. The best known of these missiles is the "Polaris," which has been used by the U.S. Navy for several years.

The guided-missile destroyer *Devonshire* firing a ship-to-air rocket from a ramp launcher at the after end of the ship.

The passenger steamship *Servia* (1881).

passenger ships

From the earliest times ships have been built to carry passengers. Usually these ships were much like those used for war or for carrying cargo. Not until steam power was applied on a commercial scale and the sailing vessel began to vanish from the seas did the modern passenger ship or ocean liner develop.

After World War I there was considerable doubt about the future of ocean liners. Many people felt that no one would want, or be able to afford, to travel in huge luxury ships at high speeds. They were, of course, wrong and many liners have been built since 1918, particularly for the voyage from Europe to America across the North Atlantic. Although it might seem that the largest of these vessels are built mainly for the prestige of their owners and their native country, and to advertise the name of the company so that its smaller liners may gain more passengers, they do in fact run at a profit.

The first ship built expressly for the Atlantic crossing was the *Oceanic,* which started making regular voyages in 1871. She was 420 feet long, 41 feet wide and had a draught of 31 feet. She was the first vessel to provide for the comforts of passengers, with lounges and cabins that extended over the whole area beneath the deck. Each cabin was light and airy and fitted with modern conveniences. The *Oceanic* also had an iron railing instead of a huge bulwark running round the edge of the deck. This allowed water to run off the deck in stormy weather. In 1888 the two steel-hulled sister ships *City of Paris* and *City of New York*, which were driven by two propellers, became the first such ships to cross the Atlantic. The *City of Paris* was 560 feet long, 53·2 feet wide and displaced 14,500 tons.

Steamers quickly became larger and more complicated. In 1899 the second *Oceanic* was built. She was longer than the *Great Eastern* at 704 feet, 68·4 feet wide, 49 feet deep and displaced 28,500 tons. Large vessels of this kind were no longer regarded with fear and apprehension. The second *Oceanic* carried no sails at all. Her sister ships *Lusitania* and *Mauretania,* launched in 1906, entered service on the transatlantic run in 1907. The *Mauretania* was even bigger than the *Oceanic*, 790 feet long, 88 feet wide, but with a draught of only 36 feet. Her seven decks were divided by fifteen bulkheads to give her 175 water-tight compartments. She was driven by four propellers from 70,000 h.p. engines, which gave her a speed of 27 knots. She had a crew of 812 and could accommodate 2,435 passengers in her three classes. The *Mauretania* won from the German steamer *Kaiser Wilhelm II* the so-called "Blue Riband" for transatlantic crossing. This prize is held by the ship which has recorded the fastest crossing between Europe and America across the Atlantic. The *Mauretania* kept it for 22 years until in 1929 the new German liner *Bremen* captured it.

66

The clipper *Flying Cloud*, the swiftest of all the American clippers. She made the voyage from New York to San Francisco around Cape Horn in 89 days, averaging a speed of 18 knots. Although she carried cargo she was basically a passenger-carrying vessel.

Between World Wars I and II there was fierce competition among the European nations to carry American tourists to Europe. One reward was that passengers would land in the ship's country of origin while they had money to spend. The Italians built the first two ships after World War I for this purpose, the *Rex* and the *Conte di Savoia*. Both were tremendously successful until the Germans replied with *Bremen* and *Europa*. These took the cream of the transatlantic trade until 1932 when the French liner *Normandie* was launched. This giant ship was 1,029 feet long (the first ship to exceed 1,000 feet in length), 117 feet wide, and had a

The 28,000-ton passenger and mail ship *Oronsay*.

draught of 36 feet. She could carry 2,170 passengers and did the trip to New York at an average speed of 31 knots.

About this time, Britain entered the contest for the Blue Riband, and the increased trade that it would bring, with the *Queen Mary*, launched in 1934. Her sister ship, *Queen Elizabeth*, did not enter passenger service until after the war in 1946, but served as a troopship during the war period. These two ships still run regular translatlantic services today. The *Queen Mary* is 1,019 feet long, 118 feet wide, weighs 81,235 tons and has a draught of 39 feet. The *Queen Elizabeth* is slightly larger at 1,031 feet. Both these liners have many luxurious facilities for passengers

The cruise liner
Braemar Castle.

The ocean liner
Rhodesia Castle

The cruise liner
Princess Kathleen.

The *Himalaya*, the second of three ships to bear this name.
She was built in 1892 and was 465 feet long with a 52 foot beam.
In her day she was a record breaker, averaging a speed of $18\frac{1}{2}$ knots.

and are fitted with roll damping fins to ensure smooth sailing. The two "Queens" have an average speed of 31 knots for the crossing from Southampton to New York, taking five days to make the crossing.

The United States did not enter the transatlantic race until after World War II when the liner *United States* made her maiden voyage in 1952. The *United States* is smaller than the "Queens" but can carry more passengers. She is 990 feet long, 101 feet wide, weighs 53,329 tons, and has accommodations for 2,008 passengers. She is capable of speeds of up to 36 knots but usually averages 30. The *United States* set two world speed records for transatlantic crossings in 1952.

Nowadays speed is not so important to liners as it was between the wars, since travellers who are in a hurry can travel by air. The modern long-distance liner puts a much greater emphasis on luxury and increased comfort for its passengers. A good example is the *Rotterdam*, the Dutch ship launched in 1958. Much shorter than the "Queen" liners, at 784 feet, she is fully air-conditioned, has twelve decks, and can carry 1,456 passengers. The *Rotterdam* has several completely new features: she has two slim exhaust funnels, and carries no fresh water on board, but distills a water supply from

The ocean liner *Empress of Canada*

The ocean liner *Oceanic*, one of the most modern vessels afloat. The first ship to bear this name was also a revolutionary craft, it was the first liner to have cabins and lounges as we understand them. The first *Oceanic* started her Atlantic run in 1871.

seawater in three evaporators which can handle 700 tons a day. Her turbine engines are situated aft to give more space for passengers. Her normal speed is 20 knots.

Another great liner on the transatlantic run is the *France*, the largest passenger liner in the world, at 1,035 feet. *France* can carry 2,000 passengers in great comfort at a speed of 31 knots. She too distills fresh water from the sea, and like the *Queen Mary* and *Queen Elizabeth* has anti-roll fins below the water line, which reduce the rolling of the ship in heavy seas to a minimum.

The latest additions to the transatlantic fleets have come from Italy and are the *Leonardo da Vinci* and *Raffaello,* two ultra-modern luxurious liners. *Raffaello* was launched in 1965 and has joined the *Leonardo da Vinci* on the Naples–New York run. The funnels are of an unusual design, whose purpose is to keep smoke and soot away from the decks. The two ships can each carry 1,775 passengers and make the Naples–New York crossing in 7 days at an average speed of 26·5 knots. They are 904 feet long, 101 feet wide and weigh 45,933 tons.

There are a number of large passenger ships which are not designed to compete with the greyhounds of the Atlantic and which carry a con-

siderable tonnage of cargo in addition to passengers. They are known as second-line ships. It should be realised that only the crack liners can afford to run without carrying any cargo. The reason they can is that they make two voyages in the same time it would take another vessel to do one. On the Atlantic run the typical second-line ships are such vessels as the *Caronia, Mauretania, America* and *Ile de France*. The long-distance runs to places like Australia and the Far East use such second-line ships as the *Pretoria Castle* (28,705 tons), *Oronsay* (27,632 tons) and the *Chusan* (24,215 tons), all averaging 22 knots. The design of these second-

The *Queen Mary* was launched in 1934 and runs on the
Southampton—New York route, making the crossing in five days.
She has 160,000 horse-power engines and an average speed of $31\frac{1}{2}$ knots.
Below, the *Queen Mary* illuminated at night.

line ships presents special problems. For example, because the vessels have to carry passengers, their cargo handling machinery—cranes, winches, derricks and other machinery—has to work quickly and silently so as not to disturb the passengers. Cargo hatches also must be so designed and placed that they do not interfere with the comfort or convenience of passengers. Further, the most modern and speedy methods of handling cargo must be used, since every additional day's loading or unloading at a port costs large sums of money.

Many passenger liners are not used on regular scheduled routes but operate as cruise liners on which passengers spend a leisurely holiday on the high seas far away from the cares of the world, occasionally stopping at ports to visit places of interest, usually for just one day. The most popular areas for this type of cruise are the Mediterranean and Caribbean.

Today's passenger ships usually carry passengers in two or three classes. The amenities, fittings, decor, menu and, of course, fare differ from class to class. The first class is nearly always placed amidships, and the cabins and public rooms are lavishly carpeted and luxuriously fitted out and decorated. The main public room is the lounge, furnished with comfortable chairs and tables. There are usually writing rooms, reading rooms, film theaters, television rooms, libraries, swimming pools and

76

The transatlantic liner *Rotterdam* one of the latest of the Atlantic giants. She can carry nearly 1,500 passengers and averages 20 knots

The ocean liner *Franconia*.

bars, as well as large dining rooms. These are usually placed on one of the lower decks, where the movement of the ship is not felt so strongly and where eating is more comfortable. Most of the cabins are placed on the outer sides of the decks so that they will have a porthole, but on very broad ships it is often necessary to have inside cabins too. First class cabins usually have beds while cabin and tourist classes have bunks, often in two tiers.

Most liners now have one or more swimming pools on open decks

77

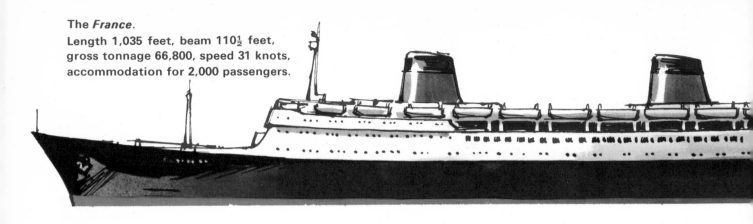

The *France*.
Length 1,035 feet, beam 110½ feet,
gross tonnage 66,800, speed 31 knots,
accommodation for 2,000 passengers.

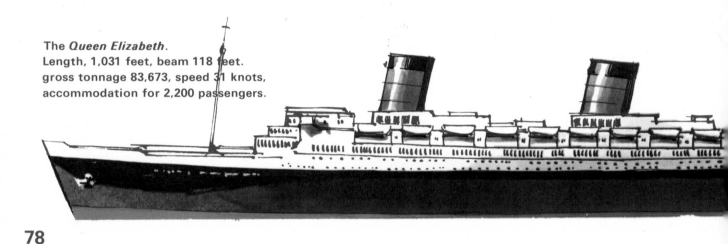

The *Queen Elizabeth*.
Length, 1,031 feet, beam 118 feet.
gross tonnage 83,673, speed 31 knots,
accommodation for 2,200 passengers.

78

The *United States*.
Length 990 feet, beam 101½ feet,
gross tonnage, 53,329, speed 30 knots,
accommodation for 2,008 passengers.

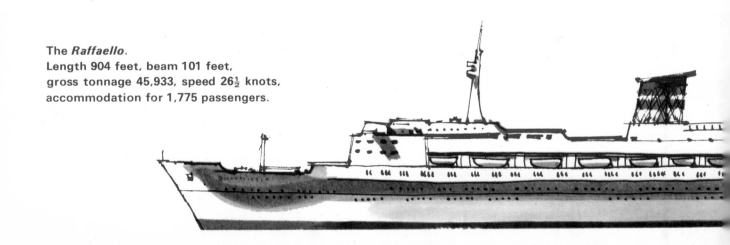

The *Raffaello*.
Length 904 feet, beam 101 feet,
gross tonnage 45,933, speed 26½ knots,
accommodation for 1,775 passengers.

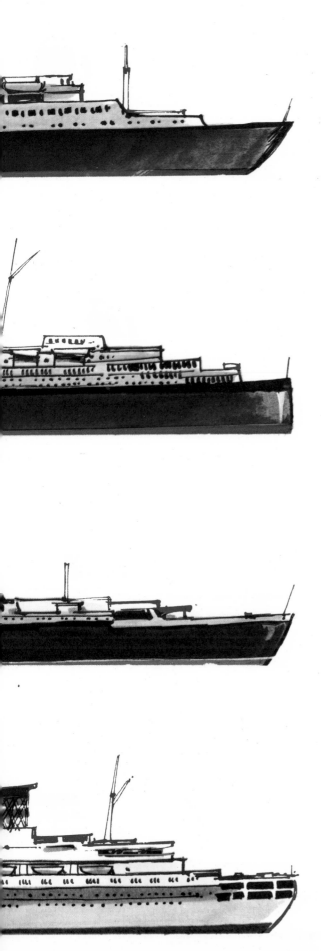

as well as areas where passengers can play a variety of games. Other parts of the decks are fitted just for sitting and relaxing in the sun, and often have large areas covered with glass for protection against bad weather.

Young people are catered to especially, and many games and competitions are organized for them. A highlight is the "crossing the line" ceremony on ships crossing the equator. If you are lucky—or unlucky—enough to be chosen, you may well be smothered in soot and ducked in the ship's pool. Most liners make special provision for children, setting aside special deck areas and rooms where they can amuse themselves away from their parents. Members of the ship's crew are usually provided to keep an eye on the children.

For entertainment in the evenings, many liners have fully equipped movie and television lounges and large ballrooms with their own orchestras so that passengers can dance, often out on deck as well as in the ballroom.

Many passenger ships which run on the less frequented routes are run as all-one-class liners, an arrangement which has proved highly successful. They are not as fast as their bigger sisters and carry some cargo as well.

Fire is one of the greatest hazards at sea, and for all the great advances

79

A panoramic view of the modern port of Genoa.

made in design and construction in recent years, this danger has still not been completely eliminated. Indicators are placed at key points in a ship and flash a warning signal to the bridge as soon as a fire breaks out. Fire may be prevented from spreading by means of fire-resisting bulkheads. Sometimes large ships carry a regular fire brigade with no other duties but to keep up a continuous patrol. Many passenger-carrying ships are fitted with sprinkler systems which discharge a fire extinguishing spray in the area of the fire and simultaneously send a fire warning to the bridge. The ideal answer to the hazard of fire is to build ships entirely of fire-resisting materials, and this is now being considered—regardless of expense.

All passenger ships carry lifeboats. These are stowed well above the passengers' heads and so do not take up any useful deck space. Passengers are required to practise boat drill fairly often so that in an emergency everyone will know where to go and what to do and will not panic. Every ship which carries more than twelve passengers must conform to a set of regulations governing the situation aboard ship in case of accident.

Cargo ships, however, may carry twelve passengers without conforming to these regulations. These ships often call at smaller ports which the large liners do not use. Travellers to these ports often prefer the convenience of sailing in this way and don't mind giving up the luxury and entertainment of a passenger liner.

merchant ships

Since the very earliest times man has used ships for trading as well as for fighting. As long ago as 1500 B.C. the Egyptians used ships for carrying cargo and passengers. These early trading vessels sailed on the Nile and the Red Sea, and some larger types sailed close to the coastline on the Mediterranean Sea as well. The ships, called "galleys," were mainly rowed by oarsmen. They were long narrow vessels steered by an extralong oar at the stern. Some types used sails in addition to oars. When Egyptian sea power dwindled, the Phoenicians, or Carthaginians, became the leading sea-faring nation. These were the people who founded the city of Carthage in North Africa. The Phoenicians traded with northern Europe and even went as far as India, a voyage which took their ships some 100 days to sail.

The power of the Phoenicians, too, waned. They were supplanted by the Greeks, who became the most powerful maritime nation. The Greeks made great advances over the sailors who had gone before them. They made charts of the oceans, and they founded colonies for trading purposes throughout the Mediterranean. Greek ships made much greater use of sail, and were the first to use their oars in banks on top of one another.

An Egyptian trading vessel of about 1,500 B.C.
It was a sea-going ship about 85 feet long and
probably traded with the people of what we now call Somaliland.

82   The Greeks were eventually defeated by the Romans. Traders from
Rome ventured as far north as the Baltic Sea for such cargoes as amber
and resin, which was used for hair dyes. The Romans also had regular
passage services around the Mediterranean. Very large ships were constructed to carry the much-needed cargoes of grain from Alexandria to
Rome. Some of these were able to carry 600 men, and were not so
different in size from cargo ships in use at the end of the nineteenth century.
After the fall of the Roman Empire there were no very startling advances
in ship building for a long time—except for the triangular "lateen" sail.

More and more, after the twelfth century, the shipping scene began to
be dominated by the northern peoples of Europe. They built ports and
their ships began to carry a much greater variety of cargoes. For a long
time, the same kind of ship, the galley, was used. But eventually a new
type of vessel was developed. This had rounded bows and stern, and
stood very high out of the water. Known as the "round ship," it had no
oars but was purely a sailing vessel.

With the "Age of Discovery" came a new kind of ship, the "galleon."
This was a cross between the "round ship" and the "galley," taking its
basic shape from the round ship but having a much greater length, like

A Roman merchantman of about 300 A.D.

the "galley." The Portuguese and Spaniards used this type of vessel for voyages of discovery and trade all over the world. All the other nations followed their example, and fierce battles for colonies and trade were fought between them. The shape of merchant vessels altered little during this period; the galleon holding its place until the appearance of steamships in the early nineteenth century.

Until modern times, ships' cargoes consisted mainly of luxuries—spices, gold, silks, ivory and the like. With the development of the industrial world this has changed. Today we depend on shipping to transport the materials necessary to our lives—oil, grain, meat, timber, cotton, coal, steel and many other materials.

Until the last few years, cargo ships could hardly have been described as other than ugly. They were also rather inefficient. Their appearance was marred by their tall, thin funnels reaching upwards so as to provide a natural draught for the furnaces. The line of the profile was scarred by the numerous derricks. The profile itself suggested the truth about the ship—that she was a floating box roughly shaped at the ends. Today, refinements in design have taken place, and these save fuel, expenses and sea time. Cargo ships have now become handsome. Graceful raking stems improve their seaworthiness and their appearance, and the funnels and bridge structures may have a degree of streamlining. Diesel machinery is more common in cargo vessels. Since World War II there has been a great increase in the number of vessels using steam turbines instead of steam reciprocating machinery.

Cargo vessels may be divided into two types, though the division between them is not as clear as it used to be. First there are the tramps. These are ships that run on no regular route. They carry various cargoes, which may at one time be coal or grain, at another time general, or bulk cargoes, between any ports where their services are required. Coal and iron ore used to be common tramp cargoes. But today these two materials, along with certain other cargoes, are usually carried in specialized ships designed to handle them with the highest efficiency both at sea and in port. With such ships the holds may be arranged to suit the cargo to be carried, and the best possible gear provided for unloading. With ships designed to carry a variety of cargoes, this is not practicable.

A "tramp" cargo vessel. These are found in all parts of the world carrying various cargoes. They have no regular route.

A motor cargo vessel, really a modern design of "tramp." These sometimes have berths for a small number of passengers.

A refrigerator ship used for transporting meat. Ships of this type steam long distances, for example, New Zealand to Britain.

An ocean-going salvage tug. Ships of this class are stationed all over the world and are equipped to aid large ships in distress. They are also used for such jobs as towing ships to breakers yards, towing floating docks and—more recently—towing floating oil derricks.

The other broad class of freight-carrying ship is the cargo liner. It differs from the tramp in working on regular routes. Cargo liners may be larger, and are usually faster, some of them attaining speeds of 20 knots. They are also designed to carry a small number of passengers, usually about a dozen, and this is a cheaper and, to many people, a more pleasant way of travelling than in a large passenger liner. In the course of a voyage they may carry a wide variety of cargoes, loading and discharging several times at various ports of call.

A specialized type of cargo vessel which is usually of the cargo liner or passenger liner type is the fruit carrier. Running to the West Indies, West Africa and the Mediterranean, these are fast, comfortable vessels of moderate size. For example, a modern banana carrier may be about 6,000 gross tons, 5,450 tons deadweight, and have a speed of 18 knots.

No cargo vessel is a clearer example of specialization than the increasingly important tanker. The earliest of them were ordinary ships with cylindrical tanks fitted into their holds. From this, in a short space of time, hastened by the tremendous world demand for oil, has been developed the highly specialized modern tanker, one of the most advanced types of cargo vessel.

Oil cargoes fall into two classes. One, known as "white oils," comprises such light and highly inflammable liquids as motor and aviation fuels. The other class, known as "black oils," includes thick crude oil, which is nearly as thick as molasses, diesel oil and the like. Several problems arise in the transport of oil cargoes. First, there is the unavoidable fire risk. It is for this reason that tankers have that well-known characteristic by which most people recognize them—the funnel far aft. This removes the source of fire to as great a distance as possible from the tanks. There is also another reason for this feature. The engines are in the stern, thus avoiding the need for the long, oil-tight shafts that would be

Oil tankers lining up to discharge their cargoes of crude oil. From the dock the oil will travel by pipe-line to the refinery.

necessary to carry the propeller shaft through the oil tanks if the engines were amidships.

Another risk is a result of the fact that oils give off gases which when mixed with air become highly explosive. During loading and discharging tankers, and when cleaning out the empty tanks, there is a danger of explosion, and rigid precautions have to be taken.

Allowance has to be made for the considerable expansion and contraction of the liquid cargo with temperature. It is essential that a large surface of oil should not be free, because of contraction, to slop from side to side, which would have a serious effect on the stability of the ship. To avoid this, fore and aft bulkheads are fitted in the tanks, which break up the free surface of the liquid. Expansion tanks may also be used. These are narrow, shallow tanks at the top of the main tanks, in which all the expansion and contraction of the cargo takes place.

Some of the most striking developments in shipbuilding have been occurring in the tanker fleets during recent years. As a result of the speed with which their liquid cargo may be loaded or discharged, they spend less time in port than other freight carriers, and the advantage of high speed at sea is that much greater. Speed is most economically achieved in big ships. It is now true that a given amount of oil may be transported more cheaply as a single cargo in one large ship than in two smaller ones. Before World War II, tankers were commonly about 11,000 tons deadweight. Now they tend to be 6–7 times this figure, and bigger vessels are in regular use. Monster tankers like the 150,000-ton *Tokyo Maru* are making their appearance. For reasons of economy in construction and propulsion, these great ships are propelled by a single engine and screw. This makes them among the most unusual ships afloat, and, because of their size, difficult to handle.

The *Tokyo Maru*, the largest vessel ever built. She is 1,005 feet long, 155 feet broad and has a displacement of 179,600 tons.

A night scene at a busy port.

90

In all types of cargo-carrying ships, including the tramps, the most striking development during the past few years has been their increase in speed. The increase cannot, of course, be compared with speeds achieved in the air, where the advances are measured in several hundreds of miles per hour. It is in the nature of the sea and ships that really high speeds by the standards of the modern world are unobtainable. The chief virtue of ships is that they can carry great loads safely rather than carrying them fast. For this reason light cargoes, like letters and other mail, watches, and small manufactured or perishable articles are carried more and more in the air. Ships, on the other hand, continue to carry the ever-growing bulk of the world's heavy commerce.

Still, it is true that speeds have increased considerably.

The *President Polk*, a freighter which also has berths for nearly a hundred passengers.

Before World War II, the typical ocean-going tramp ship would plough on her way at an average speed of 7 to 8 knots, or about twice the rate of someone walking. Now speeds of 10 to 15 knots are not unusual. The speeds of cargo liners have increased correspondingly, and may be about 15 knots for the smaller vessels and even up to 20 knots for the larger. These speeds may not seem very spectacular, but they represent a great technical achievement, for speed is one of the most expensive luxuries at sea, demanding a great increase in power and expenditure of fuel. And this has to be done so that the higher speed does not make the ship's operation so expensive that it runs at a loss. But with higher speeds money is saved because a shorter time is spent at sea and a greater number of voyages can be made in a given time. For example, a voyage from Rotterdam to New York takes about $13\frac{1}{2}$ days in a 10-knot ship, and five days less in one of 16 knots. A grain carrier sailing from Vancouver to Liverpool will take 36 days at 10 knots, 6 days less at 12 knots, and 14 days less at 16 knots. And 14 days of sea-time saved on every voyage otherwise taking five weeks is extremely valuable, even though the speed necessary to achieve this saving in time has cost a great deal of money in terms of the initial cost of the ship and her machinery, and in the fuel expended on each voyage.

The merchant fleets of the world include a great many other different type of craft from those ordinarily seen in large ports. There are the fishing trawlers, for example, which catch fish in large trawl nets dragged behind them. Now being developed are large factory trawlers which can fish for up to 80 days while processing the catch and keeping it fresh.

Related to factory trawlers are the whale factory ships, one of the largest being the *Willem Barendsz*. She is manned by a crew of 500 and has 17 whale catchers. The *Willem Barendsz* has three decks, and beneath her processing machines she has 48 tanks for storing the whale oil. She produces so much oil that other vessels have to come to her to take off oil and whale meat, and bring her fuel and supplies.

A pusher tug.

An interesting merchant ship, one which carries no cargo, is the ocean-going salvage tug. These vessels keep to stations in various parts of the world and are in constant radio contact with each other and the shore. They are ready to go to the aid of any vessel in distress and tow it to the nearest port. They are also used to tow obsolete ships to the scrap yards and assist in salvage operations on sunken ships. They carry a lot of lifting tackle and diving gear for use in salvage operations and can operate in very deep waters. Another very recent activity of these ships is towing oil- and gas-drilling rigs into position.

A considerable number of other craft are specially built for the cargo they are to carry or the job they must do. One particularly odd-looking vessel is found on rivers and lakes in the United States. This is the square-ended pusher tug, which has squared-off bows and stern used to push a number of flat barges along. Others are built for carrying timber, especially in the North Sea, taking the wood from Norway, Sweden and Finland all over Europe. These usually have their superstructure astern, leaving a long deck on which the lengths of timber are secured.

Many other varieties of working ships are found plying their way along coast lines, carrying many different kinds of cargo. These coasters are usually fairly small, since they have to use small ports and move in congested waters and do not need the power of ocean-going vessels. Some of these are very similar to barges which take cargoes inland from coastal ports up rivers and canals to factories and warehouses.

Ferries are another kind of merchant vessel. They can be of many types. Simple passenger ferries are used to cross rivers where there are no bridges. These are often paddle-driven, and may sometimes be guided by a chain which is attached to either bank and passes through a runnel on the ferry. These small ferries frequently carry a few automobiles too. They are usually flat, with their superstructure to one side. They have gates at each end for cars to drive on and off, and through which passengers may pass.

A Baltic timber carrier.

A coastal tanker.

Capturing the thrill of sail.

boats for pleasure

Sailing is almost as old as man himself, but it was not until after the First World War that it became popular as a pastime. Since then thousands of people have bought themselves small boats in which they sail in races or just for fun.

Power boats, too, have become popular, and great numbers are seen around the coasts on summer weekends. The engines used in these craft fall into two main categories. The inboard engine, which is built into the structure of the boat, is a smaller version of the engine used in bigger ships. The outboard engine is fixed onto the stern of the boat and can be easily removed. The outboard engine consists of a motor and a shaft with a propeller at its base. This shaft can be turned so that the propeller turns, and then the boat is steered as well as propelled by its engine. Many small pleasure craft can be used either as sailing or power boats, either by being built to accommodate both engines and sails, or by simply fixing a small outboard engine to the stern of a sailing boat.

Modern power boats achieve very high speeds, and new ones are being built that will go even faster. One new kind of very fast power boat has a conventional engine in the stern, and also a hovercraft engine at its bows. As the boat moves forward air is sucked in through vents in its bows and blown out again by a fan. The air which is blown out is

97

Speed boat powered by twin engines.

98   **High-speed power boats in an
international race. Such boats can achieve
an average speed of 28 miles per hour.**

caught under the bows, causing them to rise out of the water and ride on a cushion of air. This allows the conventional engine at the stern to develop greater speeds than it could with the entire weight of the boat to push through the water.

Many enthusiasts build their own boats nowadays, and several large companies supply boat kits from which a boat can be constructed. A large number of power boats have moulded fiberglass hulls which make them much lighter than boats constructed in the usual manner of timbers covered with plywood. A number of long distance power boat races are held each year. The most famous of these is the international race sponsored by the *Daily Express* from the Isle of Wight to Torquay, across the South Coast of England. Americans are keen competitors in this race and one of them, Dick Bertram, won the 1965 race. He covered the 198 miles in just under seven hours at an average speed of over 28 m.p.h.

Increasing numbers of larger motor powered cruisers are also becoming popular. They have good accommodation for a family and are much used for holidays on rivers and in coastal waters. They are usually more solidly built than the faster power boats, and many are suitable for short sea trips.

Sailing boats are still the most numerous of the pleasure boats. They come in a variety of shapes and sizes ranging from 10-feet long dinghies to the huge 70-feet long yachts used in the America's Cup races.

The smallest group, the dinghies, are tremendously popular. They are light and easily fixed to a trailer and pulled along behind a car. They are reasonably cheap to buy and are very easy to maintain. Dinghies are great fun to sail. Because they sit so low in the water they give a great impression of speed although actually moving relatively slowly.

This high-speed boat incorporates in its bows the hovercraft principle to lift the nose off the water and so reduce the resistance or drag of the water.

They do not usually have cabins, although some of the larger classes have some kind of shelter.

The hulls of dinghies are constructed in a variety of ways. Clinker-built boats have overlapping strips of wood nailed to a framework of ribs which stick up from the middle timber or keel. When the planks butt up to one another and present a flat surface, this is known as carvel built. Moulded hulls may be of wood strips held together with strong glues, or of fiberglass, made up over a master mould. Plywood hulls are making a great contribution to boat building since the plywood parts can be prefabricated and then assembled at home by the enthusiast.

Dinghies usually have two triangular sails, a small foresail or jib attached to a cable running from the masthead to the bows, and a larger mainsail which is attached to the mast and to a horizontal boom which pivots from the mast. The boom will swing from side to side of the boat to catch the wind from whichever direction it is blowing. It needs to be carefully watched by the crew, and many a sailor has had a nasty bump on the head, or been knocked overboard, by a swinging boom. The sails are controlled by ropes or sheets. The mainsail is controlled by the helmsman, who also steers the boat with the rudder. The jib in a two-man dinghy is controlled by the crewman, who may sometimes be seen balancing on a sliding seat or a trapeze wire to keep the boat upright. Many dinghies may also have a third sail, the spinnaker. The spinnaker is an extra foresail which is attached to the mast and has two sheets which are made fast to the sides of the dinghy. It presents a balloon-like

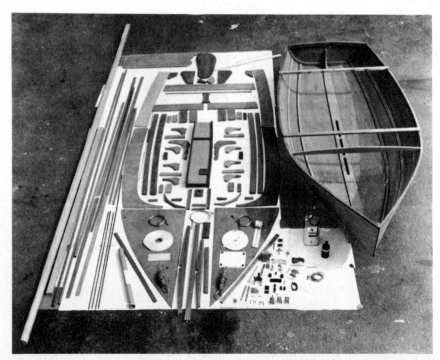

A do-it-yourself kit for a small dinghy. Such kits provide a boat at the lowest cost, and also teach the basis of boat building —an essential for all young enthusiasts.

appearance, for it is only used when running before the wind. Since it can catch a lot of wind, it gives considerable extra speed to the dinghy.

Dinghy racing is an exciting sport in which success depends more on the skill of the crew than the size and speed of the boat. Many races are limited to dinghies of the same class, which depends on length and sail area. In these races the helmsman's skill is all-important. Other races are between boats that vary in size and design. The competition between these different kinds of dinghies has resulted in many improvements in design, as the most efficient designs have done best.

Yachts differ from dinghies in that they have fixed keels and therefore need much more water in which to sail than dinghies, which can sail in as little as three or four feet of water. Yachts also vary in size from about 20 feet to 70 feet. Pure racing yachts have little cabin space and are used in sheltered offshore courses or inshore. Larger ocean racing yachts are provided with much more in the way of accommodation, as they undertake long sea voyages and are in effect cruisers with an

Racing dinghies with spinnakers set.

Crews well out to keep dinghies upright.

Left, the American *Constellation* and the British *Sovereign* competing in the most sought after of prizes—the America's Cup. The race was originally won by the American schooner *America* in 1851 at Cowes, Isle of Wight. The keen competition for this trophy has done much to advance the design and construction of yachts.

emphasis on speed. Cruising yachts are often built to their owner's specification and therefore vary considerably in size and tonnage. Yachts

are heavier and less exciting to sail than dinghies, they need larger crews, and unlike dinghies, sail better heeled over than upright.

The largest yachts of a recognised class are the 12 metre (70 feet) long vessels which, among other races, compete for the famous America's Cup. This race, first held in 1851, grew out of the Great Exhibition in London, at which the Royal Yacht Squadron presented a silver cup for a 60 mile race round the Isle of Wight. The trophy is decided by the best of seven races over the same course. In the first race the United States' yacht *America* won the trophy. Britain has never recaptured it, although sixteen attempts have been made. Canada has tried twice and Australia once. In the 1965 race, *Constellation* beat the British challenger *Sovereign* in four straight races.

Yacht racing also is a part of the Olympic Games, where there are competitions for several classes of yachts with large crews, as well as for single-handed and two-man crews.

In the realm of dinghies and small yachts a new design has appeared in the western world. This is the catamaran, which seems quite new but is actually related to a similar vessel used for many years in the South Pacific islands. The catamaran has two hulls which resemble canoes,

Far left: a "Dragon" class yacht.
Middle left: a "Flying Fifteen."
Left: 5.5 meter yachts.

which are joined by a flat deck on which the mast is supported. A centerboard, or removable keel, drops through this deck. Catamarans are very fast, and very wet for the crew, since water from inside the hulls sprays over the bridge deck where the crew sits. Catamarans were slow to be accepted by traditional yachtsmen, but are now becoming a familiar sight on sailing waters and compete in races organized for them. A further refinement of the catamaran is the three-hulled trimaran, which has two bridge decks.

Anyone who has a boat, no matter how big a yacht or how small a dinghy, must of course understand at least the rudiments of sailing before giving himself up to the fates of the wind and water. There are three basic sailing methods—running before the wind, close-hauled, and reaching. In all three, the position of the sails in relation to the wind and the boat is most important.

First, running before the wind: in this method the boat is moving in the same direction in which the wind is blowing. The mainsail is held out almost at right angles to the boat to catch as much wind as possible, and the force of the wind coming from the rear propels the vessel forward. Since the sail must be to one side of the boat, it will tend to move sideways slightly as well as forward. This is known as leeway. To counteract it the rudder of the boat must be put over opposite the

Cruiser-racers with full spinnakers
at the start of an off-shore race.

sail, to keep the bows pointing in the desired direction. Running before
a fairly good wind an extra sail, the spinnaker, is often set centrally across
the bows. When there is very little wind, known as "light airs", it may
be necessary to hold the main boom to one side and the jib to the other
side of the boat to make any progress. Running before the wind is not
the most exciting method of sailing and does not result in great speeds.
It can be dangerous, too, as a violent gust could topple the boat stern
over bows.

In the second method, sailing close-hauled, the boat is going against
the direction the wind is blowing, that is, sailing right into the wind. It
is perhaps a little difficult to understand how a yacht or dinghy can make
progress against the wind. The point is that a boat cannot possibly sail

An ocean-going trimaran.
Like the catamaran this is
a very fast boat capable
of making over 20 knots.

directly into the wind. To sail close-hauled the boat must make a series of tacks. Tacking into the wind is accomplished by pulling the sails in tightly almost in a straight line fore and aft, with the bows of the boat pointing at about 45 degrees to the direction from which the wind is blowing. The wind acts on the outside curve of the sails and produces a forward thrust by creating a vacuum in the same way as the air passage around the wing of a plane causes an upward lift. The wind blowing on the windward side of the sails also tends to heel the boat over, so that the crew in a dinghy will need to lean out on the opposite side to keep it upright. Great care must be taken when changing the direction of tacking, that is "going about". If the boat is going at too slow a speed, when the bows come straight into the wind, the boat will stop and may even start to drift backwards. This is a most embarrassing experience. Close-hauled sailing is probably the most difficult to control. But it can often be very fast, is always exhilarating, and frequently, very wet, as the crew are exposed to spray thrown up by the wind and by the bows smashing through the wave crests.

108

In the third method, reaching, the boat is sailing with the wind blowing across its course instead of directly into its course, as in the close-hauled method. Reaching is the fastest method of sailing, and the force of the wind is used in the same way as when sailing close-hauled. When the sails are held in almost close-hauled position, this is known as a close

A modern ocean racer.

The hull of a boat under construction.

A large family catamaran.

A racing catamaran.

12-meter yachts.

reach. When the wind is further astern, the sails are set nearer to the "before the wind" position, and this is called broad reaching. It is usually necessary to put the rudder over slightly to counteract the leeway, although less leeway is made when reaching than when close-hauled. Frequently, in reaching, the bows will lift out of the water and the boat will be planing along the surface almost like a hydrofoil.

After learning the basic principles of sailing a beginner should be able to handle a dinghy without much trouble. But only through practice and the example of an experienced helmsman can he learn complete control of the vessel under any conditions of wind and sea. It will probably be some time before you are sufficiently able a helmsman to cross the Atlantic on your own, but even this feat has been achieved in very small boats.

A modern cruiser sailer.

Robert Manry in his tiny boat *Tinkerbelle* on the lone Atlantic
voyage from Falmouth, Massachusetts, to Falmouth, England.

The underwater craft *Alvin* used for deep-sea
research. She has a two-man crew and in 1965 made
a record-making dive of 6,000 feet in just under three hours.

new and unusual ships

So far we have looked at fighting, passenger and cargo ships. Besides these there are many other types of boat, some of which have been developed in recent years and are in many ways revolutionary. For example, there is the hovercraft, which glides above the surface of the sea but which is primarily a marine craft. Then again, there are the small underwater craft, looking more like giant crabs than anything else, which are now being used extensively for exploration under the sea.

One ship which looks very much like an ordinary cargo vessel but is in fact a truly revolutionary ship is the N.S. *Savannah*. Ever since marine engineers began to use steam power to drive ships some 160 years ago, they have dreamed of a fuel which could produce steam for an indefinite period of time. This has partly been achieved with the nuclear ship *Savannah*. This pace-making craft has a clipper bow and a graceful, streamlined superstructure. She is 595 feet long, 78 feet wide and draws $29\frac{1}{2}$ feet of water. Fully loaded, she displaces 20,000 tons. Although in every way a modern cargo ship, she carries berths for

113

The nuclear-powered merchantship *Savannah*. She can carry 9,500 tons of freight and has accommodation for 60 passengers. Once her atomic reactor is loaded she can steam for some 300,000 nautical miles without needing to refuel.

A lightship on duty.

passengers. The nuclear power plant drives steam turbines which develop 22,000 horsepower and can maintain a cruising speed of approximately 21 knots. The reactor core contains 17,000 pounds of uranium and has a life of about three years. This means that the *Savannah* is capable of making twelve voyages around the earth on one radio-active charge.

An unusual type of vessel, concerned with safety at sea, is the lightship. She has no engines with which to propel herself but is towed into position and moored to a fixed station to warn other ships of such dangers as isolated rocks, shoals or sandbanks. The lightship is used where it is not possible to build a permanent lighthouse. She must stay on station all the time, and her crew must be on watch day and night until they are relieved. A lightship carries a powerful light which is mounted on gimbals, a system of pivots, to keep the beam level however much the ship rolls and tosses in the sea.

Another unusual ship with a very essential job is the motor lifeboat which is always ready to go to the rescue of all ships in distress. This is a very hazardous job, and the crews need to be highly skillful. Lifeboats carry a lot of gear to help them in their often dangerous work: radio-telephones for talking to air-sea rescue aircraft and helicopters, search-lights, loud hailers (megaphones), oil sprays for calming the sea, navigation and radar equipment and rescue rocket apparatus. The lifeboat's engines are completely sealed so that they will work when the boat is awash, they can be switched from "full ahead" to "full astern" instantly, as the lifeboat tries to draw close to a rolling ship. In the rare event of capsizing, the modern motor lifeboat can right herself in about seven seconds or less.

A weather and ocean research ship.

A motor life-boat going to the
aid of a ship in distress.

The Russian hydrofoil ship *Meteor*.

The weather ship is another type of unusual but important ship. Normally weather ships keep to a fixed station and their crews record meteorological data which they radio back to weather observatories on land. This information is essential in accurate weather forecasting, which is, of course, vital for everyone, whether at sea, on the land or in the air. Often, however, weather ships have to go to the rescue of ships in distress, especially far out at sea and beyond the reach of the normal lifeboat service.

The hard-worked donkey of the marine world is undoubtedly the tug. It is needed for the simple reason that it is difficult for big ships to steer their way through narrow channels and other vessels in a port. The tug has a towing hook fixed amidships which is specially made to take up any sudden strain. The crew is protected from the danger of the whiplash of a broken cable by "strongbacks", which are broad metal loops that arch across the decks over the cables. The towing hook is fitted with a release catch which, when it is knocked out, releases the cable immediately. The release catch is used when, for example, a towing cable runs foul of another ship. The towing operation is directed from the bridge of the ship being towed. The job of the tug is only finished when the ship is safely berthed.

An odd-looking craft that can be seen in rivers, estuaries, and at docks is the dredge. This vessel has very important jobs to do in keeping silt and debris out of navigation channels at docks, coastal waters, rivers, canals and estuaries. The equipment carried by the dredge falls into

Tugs in action. These hard-working boats are mostly used in ports and docks. For their size they are powerful vessels, most of whose space is used for housing machinery and other gear.

The Russian icebreaker *Lenin*. She has three nuclear reactors driving steam turbines which generate 44,000 horse power. At a speed of 2 knots she can break ice 8 feet thick.

The deep-sea explorer *Aluminaut* built of
6-inch slabs of aluminium to withstand the
enormous pressures of the ocean at great depths.
She can stay submerged for about 30 hours.

three main kinds, depending on the type of silt to be removed. For near-fluid silt, flexible tubes are lowered on derricks into the silt, which is sucked up and run into storage tanks called "hoppers." When these are full, the dredge moves out into deep water and dumps the silt through an underwater door. The second type of dredge uses heavy mechanical shovels mounted on the forward deck and also stores silt in hoppers, which are emptied in deep water where silt will not interfere with shipping channels. Sometimes completely new channels need to be cut, and for this job the dredge is equipped with a continuously moving chain of buckets which scoop up huge mouthfuls of debris that is later dumped into deep water.

Some of the most exciting craft to be developed in recent years are those for underwater exploration; the best known of these have been designed and tested by the French pioneer of underwater exploration, Jacques Yves Cousteau. These new types of craft are not just being developed to observe the plant and animal life of the sea; they have very essential and practical applications to man's material needs. They are being used to explore the sea as a possible source of minerals and food.

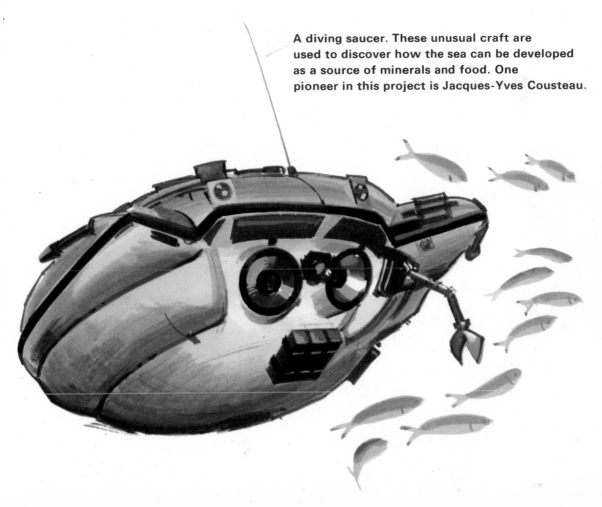

A diving saucer. These unusual craft are used to discover how the sea can be developed as a source of minerals and food. One pioneer in this project is Jacques-Yves Cousteau.

The cable-laying ship *Cable Enterprise*. She has unwinding gear fore and aft.

Cousteau is engaged in a vast and imaginative research project. His teams of divers and scientists have lived for weeks at a time in the ocean depths. They use both fixed underwater houses and fascinating two-man diving saucers with a steel and fiberglass hull. The saucers are steered by pumping water at high pressure through steering jets. Crew members lie on foam-rubber couches and observe through two windows. Each saucer is equipped with very powerful lights and a remote control mechanical claw that enables the crew to remove and examine specimens from the seabed.

The latest deep-sea explorer is the "Aluminaut," constructed of six-inch-thick slabs of aluminium which give the vessel strength enough to withstand enormous pressures without making it too heavy. The low weight gives the "Aluminaut" a great buoyancy, allowing it to operate at very great depths. It can stay submerged for about thirty hours, travels at four knots and has a range of eighty miles. It is also equipped with powerful television cameras, sonar and communication apparatus.

Across the ocean bed stretch cables which link continent with continent. These cables allow peoples at opposite sides of the world to communicate with each other. Although the cables have several protective coatings, they do wear out and must continually be repaired. A group of ships called "cable-layers" have the sole task of laying new cables and maintaining existing ones. The biggest cable-laying ship in the world is the *Long Lines*. This is an apt name, for she can lay 2,000 miles of cable in one operation. Her cable deck and gear are all under cover, a necessary precaution in northern waters. The cable is stored in circular tanks which are each three decks deep, and four supplementary tanks hold about 100 miles of repair cable. She also carries several tons of grapnels, buoys and ropes. *Long Lines* can lay cable both over her stern and bows. When a cable is laid over the stern, it is drawn out by revolving caterpillar tracks which part automatically to allow the repeaters to pass through freely. (Repeaters are incorporated in cables to boost the power of the signals on their journey and are more bulky than the cable itself). A cable ship needs very accurate navigational instruments in order to pinpoint its position over a cable on the seabed, and for this reason the *Long Lines* has twelve separate position-fixing devices.

Keeping open communication lines of an entirely different order is the job of icebreakers. One icebreaker of more than normal interest is the Russian nuclear-powered icebreaker *Lenin*. She is the largest icebreaker afloat, and her unlimited range allows her to take convoy after convoy from Murmansk to Vladivostok when the Arctic Ocean freezes over during the northern winter. By keeping open this 5,800-mile-long channel, the *Lenin* saves convoys the trouble of taking an alternative

A bucket and chain type dredge. These vessels are used for keeping open or deepening waterways.

and much longer route. There are icebreakers at work in the Antarctic, too, allowing men, equipment and supplies to be ferried to the people who now live semi-permanently in the frozen wastes around the South Pole carrying out invaluable scientific research. Icebreakers are con-structed for tremendous strength, and their specially shaped bows ride up over the ice and crush it with their great weight. In this way they can smash through ice up to twenty feet deep. Most icebreakers are fitted with multiple engines, often diesel-electric, for rapid propeller response when moving through ice. The propellers and shafts are excep-tionally strong and well protected. Some icebreakers have forward-facing propellers at their bows to make it easier for them to turn in the ice and force the broken ice astern of them. If an icebreaker becomes trapped herself, she can get free by pumping water from one side of the ship to the other through "heeling" tanks and thus rolling from side to side.

The hydrofoil is one of the most recent advances in marine engineering. Its design enables the craft to achieve very high speeds. It has underwater fins or wings which skim along the surface when the boat has gathered speed, keeping the hull well above water-level. The engines, no longer having to push the craft's weight through the water, are free to use all their power for increasing speed. In this way the hydrofoil can travel much faster and do more work than a conventional boat with the same size engines.

A passenger-carrying hovercraft of the type used for trips of about 30 to 50 miles. Larger machines are being designed for service on transatlantic and other long distance runs.

A hovercraft on patrol. This type of craft can operate in conditions which no other type of vessel could, for example, swamps, unnavigable rivers and deserts.

Hydrofoils are in service as passenger carriers on Russia's inland waterways. Some like the *Sputnik* can achieve speeds of forty knots even though carrying a full load of three hundred passengers. They are also in use in many other countries all over the world. Many countries are testing hydrofoils for use as naval offshore patrol boats and anti-submarine vessels. Small hydrofoil launches have successfully made the crossing of the North Sea from England to Holland, and on the drawing boards of many nations are plans for large nuclear-powered versions. These, it is hoped, will be able to cross the oceans carrying huge loads

of cargo, or great numbers of passengers in complete safety and comfort, under any conditions.

One of the most revolutionary craft of recent years is the "hovercraft", which is now being rapidly developed for both commercial and especially military use. The first hovercraft, which underwent its trials in 1959, looks rather like a very broad, flat-bottomed boat with a wide, squat funnel in the middle. But no smoke comes out of this funnel. Instead, large quantities of air are sucked into it by means of a fan driven by an engine. This air is delivered through two large circular slots, called "annular jets," to the space beneath the vessel. Each annular jet provides a cushion of air enclosing a large area beneath the floor of the craft. The cushion of air which is trapped underneath the craft is contained by a flexible rubber skirt that runs round the craft. Now, the air does not pass downwards vertically. Instead it is directed slightly inwards so that when the air reaches the ground it fills up the space inside the circle instead of escaping outward. The air then develops a series of eddies, going round and round like rollers, until the pressure is so great that no more air can squeeze in. By this time, the pressure is high enough to lift the entire vessel clear of the level of the sea, where it hovers safely on its cushion of air. It can now be driven along by means of propellers or jets on the sides of the vessel, the latter being supplied with some of the high-pressure air from the fan. The hovercraft moves very easily because there is no friction between the bottom of the vessel and the water, as there is when a ship's hull ploughs through the sea.

A naval patrol boat cutting through the water.
This high-speed craft is powered by gas-turbine engines.

A "jangada" of Brazil. It is
made of logs strapped
together and fitted with
a simple sail. Craft
of this kind are used
by coastal fishermen.

Two dhows with sails
rigged. This kind of vessel
is used in coastal waters,
rivers and canals for carrying
almost every type of cargo.

A New Guinea "lakatoi." This type of vessel
consists of several dug-out canoes lashed together
and covered with a bamboo platform of up to 50 feet.

The Western world has no monopoly of strange, exotic craft. One of the most striking of these is the "lakotoi" of New Guinea. It is usually constructed of three large dug-out canoes lashed together side-by-side, supporting a platform and rough cabins. The sails are of woven matting and are supported on two masts amidships. The people who sail these primitive boats have an innate sense of seamanship which enables them to make long voyages out of sight of land with little or no navigational equipment.

Recently Thor Heyerdahl and a crew of Scandinavians constructed a replica of a primitive balsa log raft, called *Kon Tiki*. They launched their raft, put themselves at the mercy of the Trade Winds and the Pacific Ocean currents and sailed for 101 adventurous and often perilous days, covering 5,000 miles, until they were finally shipwrecked on the Polynesian island of Raroia. This was not just a sea adventure but a scientific expedition to prove that the original inhabitants of the Polynesian islands came from South America.

Thor Heyerdahl's raft, the *Kon Tiki*. It was made of balsa wood and of a design similar to that used by early South American sailors.

A single-masted sambuk, often called a dhow. Ships of this type are still common in the Red Sea and other Arabian waters.

index